ALL SAIN

CU00760067

13-15

6 ■ **Never Ever**

12 ■ **Bootie Call**

17 ■ **I Know Where It's At**

24 ■ **Under The Bridge**

28 ■ **Heaven**

34 ■ **Alone**

39 ■ **If You Want To Party** (I Found Lovin')

46 ■ **Trapped**

51 ■ **Beg**

58 ■ **Lady Marmalade**

63 ■ **Take The Key**

68 ■ **War Of Nerves**

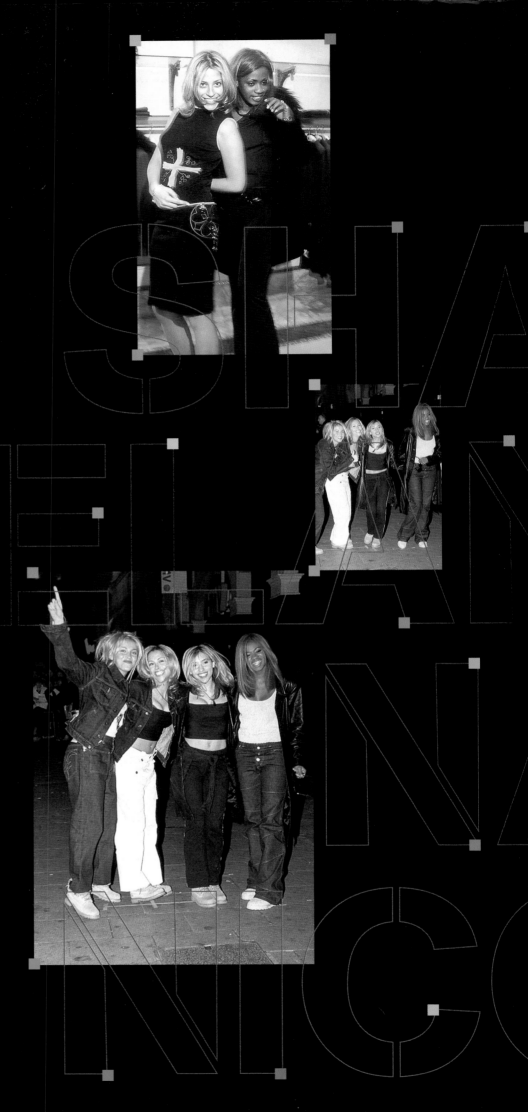

Distributors:
Music Sales Limited
8/9 Frith Street, London W1V 5TZ, England.

Music Sales Pty Limited
120 Rothschild Avenue, Rosebery,
NSW 2018, Australia.

Order No.AM953535
ISBN 0-7119-7154-4

Visit the Internet Music Shop at
http://www.musicsales.co.uk

Music arranged by Roger Day.
Music processed by
Paul Ewers Music Design.
Photos courtesy of
London Features International.

Printed in the United Kingdom by
Caligraving Limited, Thetford, Norfolk.

Never Ever

Words & Music by Shaznay Lewis
Music by Rickidy Raw

(Spoken) A few questions that I need to know, how you could ever hurt me so, I need to know what I've done wrong, and how long it's been going on. Was it that I never paid enough attention, or did I not give enough affection? Not only will your answers keep me sane, but I'll know never to make the same mistake again. You can tell me to my face

or even on the phone, you can write it in a letter, either way I have to know. Did I never treat you right

did I always start the fight? Either way I'm going out of my mind, all the answers to my questions I have to find.

1. My head's spin - ning, — boy I'm in — a daze, — I feel i - so - lat - ed,
(Verse 2 see block lyric)

don't want to com - mun - i - cate. — I'll take a show - er, I will — scour, — I will run —

find peace of mind, the hap-py mind, I once owned yeah.

Flex-in' vo-cab-u-la-ry runs right through me. The al-pha-bet runs right from A to Z.

Con-ver-sa-tions, hes-i-ta-tions in my mind, you got my con-science ask-ing ques-tions that I can't find

I'm not cra-zy. I'm sure I ain't done no-thing wrong. No,

I'm just wait - ing, 'cause I heard that this feel - ing won't last___ that long.___

Nev - er ev - er have I ev - er felt so low, when you gon - na take me out of this black hole.

Nev - er ev - er have I ev - er felt so sad. The way I'm feel - ing, yeah you got me feel - ing real - ly bad.

Nev - er ev - er have I had to find, I've had to dig a - way to find my own peace of mind.

Verse 2:

I keep searching deep within my soul
For all the answers, don't wanna hurt no more.
I need peace, got to feel at ease, need to be
Free from pain, go insane, my heart aches.

Sometimes vocabulary runs through my head
The alphabet runs right from A to Z
Conversations, hesitations in my mind.
You got my conscience asking questions that I can't find
I'm not crazy
I'm sure I ain't done nothing wrong
Now I'm just waiting
'Cause I heard that this feeling won't last that long.

11

Bootie Call

Words & Music by Shaznay Lewis
Music by Karl Gordon

al-ways fin-ish what you start ba - by and al-ways hav-in' you beg for more.

You know I wan-na be dig-gy down— boy, but I— don't get— a - round,

Jim-my hitched a ride in your pock-et I lock him in your wal-let, it's just— a boo-tie call.

D.%. al Coda

%. *Coda*

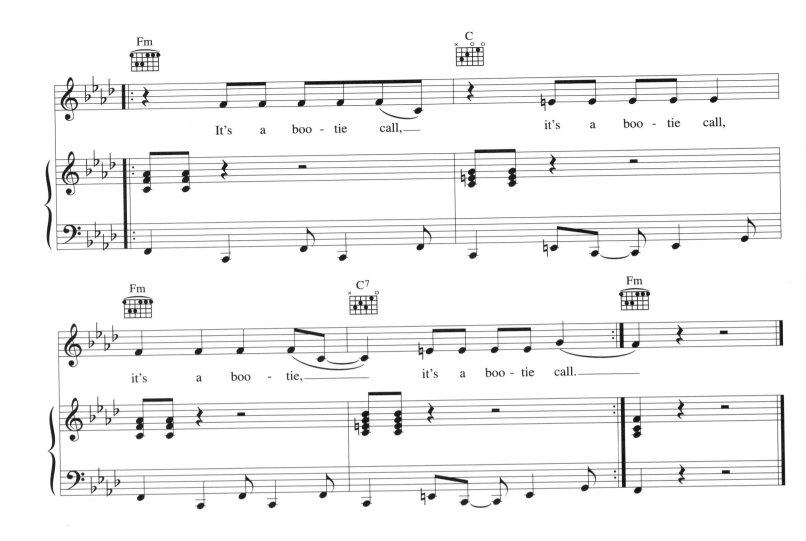

Verse 2:
I'm keen on you what is baby
Some things are always good to have
You never let me down
I'm always happy when you make me laugh
But don't try to find
This heart of mine
Emotions don't come into my head
So don't be misled, my heart doesn't need to be bled.

Only trying to be smart babe
Don't need the rollercoaster ride
I've been and seen and done it all yeah
Don't want you messing with my mind
So don't be a fool
Keep this as your number one rule:
Good loving's not always from the heart
You got to be smart, stay just the way you are.

I Know Where It's At

Words & Music by Shaznay Lewis, Karl Gordon,
Walter Becker, Donald Fagen & Paul Griffin

want to have a good time,— if you know you've got some-thing on your

mind,— if you know that you wan-na get on down,— don't de-

-ny it, don't be shy,——— just come a - round.—

1. I've— been watch-ing you— and I know— you like— to par-ty ba - by,
(Verse 2 see block lyric)

So if you're feel-ing kind-a low well ba-by don't,—— 'cause I'll be

If you

here right by your side, rea-dy to flow.—— If you

want to have a good time,— if you know you've got some-thing on your

mind,— if you know that you wan-na get on down,— don't de-

- ny it don't be shy _____ just come a - round. _

1, 2, 3, 4, Saints in the house.

We know where it's at.   We know where it's at.

Well if you know you like to party and you want to get on down, let me tell you baby that you've come to the right town.

'Cause it's party time you've got to get your groove on,   I know you wanna jam from night to dawn.

Baby got it goin' on, I don't see nothing wrong, you dance pretty hot and I know you'll like my song,

So move it like that, rat-a-tat-tat, now we'll confirm that you know where it's at. Just come a - round.— If you

want to have a good time,— if you know you've got some-thing on your

mind,— if you know that you wan-na get on down,— don't de -

Verse 2:
Move around and get on down, do what you wanna baby,
You gotta be good, you gotta be good and ready to go.
I know you've been waiting for my party all your lifetime baby
Everybody in the whole world wants to know.

Can't you see that there's no-one on the streets
'Cos everybody knows where they've got to be.

Under The Bridge

Words & Music by Anthony Kiedis,
Flea, John Frusciante & Chad Smith

1. Some - times I feel like I don't have a fath - er. Some-times I feel like
(Verses 2 & 3 see block lyrics)

like I did that day,   take me   to   the place   I   love,   take me   all   the way.

To Coda

1, 4.   4º D.%. al Coda   2.

one time… two time…

3.   D.%.

three time…   four time…

Verse 2:
I drive on the streets, 'cause he's my companion
I walk through his fields, 'cause he knows who I am.
He sees my good deeds then he kisses me windy
I never worried, now that is a lie.

Verse 3:
It's hard to believe, there's nobody out there
It's hard to believe that I'm all alone.
At least I have his love, the city he loves me
Lonely as I am, together we cry.

Heaven

Words & Music by Shaznay Lewis, Melanie Blatt,
Natalie Appleton, Nicole Appleton, Cameron McVey & Magnus Fiennes

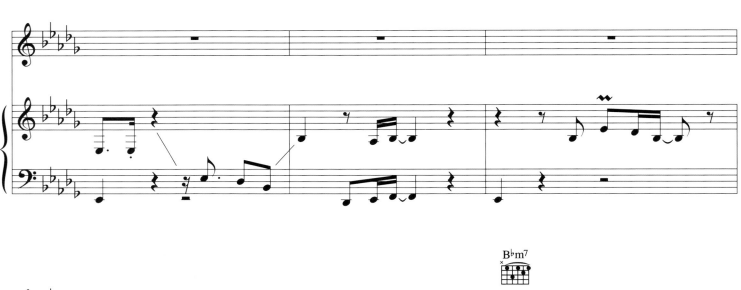

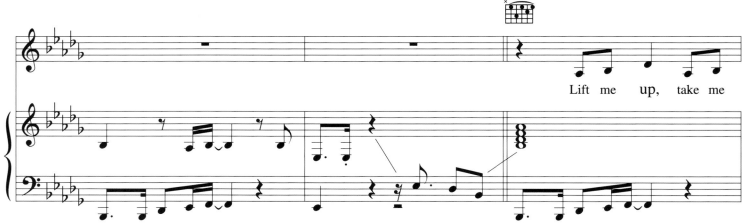

Lift me up, take me

1. Scared to laugh,_____ scared to cry,_____ for fear_ of_____
(Verse 2 see block lyric)

_____ my own con - tra - dic - tion. May - be I_____ should try_

_____ and cov-er mor - al rea - sons. For god - sakes,_ hea-ven lift me up_

Verse 2:
Take me high
Above the clouds where the birds fly.
I'm feeling free
Let heaven do the work for me.
Looking over this crazy city
Where we're living
I've seen it, done it
It's just the way I've been.

*Bridge (**D.%**)*
I won't fake
I won't break
No way
No.

Alone

Words & Music by Shaznay Lewis
Music by Karl Gordon

Not gon-na, don't wan-na, nev-er gon-na, don't wan-na, wan-na end up a-lone.

Not gon-na, nev-er gon-na, don't—

don't wan-na, wan-na end up a - lone.

1. I need to sit back and kick out, it's a - bout— the way I'm mak-ing you
(Verse 2 see block lyric)

feel. You're

tryin' to show me— that you're hap-py, real-ly hap-py, but I can see that you're feel-ings aren't for

real.   The un - hap -

- pi - ness I may be caus - in' you is de - fin - it - ely un - in - ten - tion - al.

So don't hes -

- i - tate, don't be a - fraid to tell me 'cause my ac - tions are not per -

Not gon - na,—— don't wan - na,—— not gon - na, don't wan - na, don't know.

Oh,   no,   oh.

Verse 2:

I need you to be honest, really honest
And tell me what's on your mind.
Whatever the problem may be
You tell me, oh 'cause the body never lies.
Am I too hard, too soft
Or am I really just selfish to the bone?
So don't hesitate, I'm a psychic babe
Let your feelings all be known…
…but I'll tell you something right now.

If You Want To Party (I Found Lovin')

Words & Music by Michael Walker & Johnny Flippin

Kick - ing it live, keep - ing it real, driv - ing on time, yeah you know how you feel. You

got - ta get up— and move side to side,— you got - ta re - lease— and do it right,— it's a

funk - a - de - lic beat to a funk - a - de - lic soul, still kick - ing it live with the main man's— Jon

Saints in the house, yeah we're do - in' it right, a cool rock - in' jam and par - ty all night, so

(Verse 2 see block lyric)

let's get start-ed ba-by you and I, go on with your bad self dance all night, so

can you feel it, I can feel it, hey, give it to the beat, go the bass drum, boom-in' in your

feet hear the snare drum tap-pin' in your ear. Yeah, you got-ta get up,— got-ta move your rear.

That's the way this heart is a feel-ing for you,—————— 'cause

To Coda

no one does it bet - ter,＿ look there ain't no doubt, just what I wan - na do,＿

_＿＿＿＿＿＿ so won't you let me sweat ya?＿ Let's get

start - ed if you want to par - ty, ba - by it's just you and me, I've got

what you need,＿ don't con - ceal it, tell me you can feel it, won't you let me

Verse 2 (D.%.):
So on and on and on, on and on and on
Check it check it check it out to the break the break of dawn.
Ask the bass drum, stick it to your ear, can you hear?
Move your rear, wind your body to the beautiful snare.
Guys grab a girl and take her from the back
And give it up, give it up, 'cause we like it like that
Girls grab a guy, show him that you ain't feeling shy
Keep it going as the bridge comes back in time.

Trapped

Words & Music by Neville Henry,
Karen Gibbs, Shaznay Lewis & Melanie Blatt

One two, one two she's trapped, gon-na need some help, what you think a-bout that? One two, one two she's trapped, gon-na need some help, what you think a-bout that? One two, one two she's what, gon-na need some help, what you think a-bout that? One

two,   one two   she's trapped,   gon-na need some help.

1. She sits   in her arm - chair,____   look-ing   in - to space,
(Verse 2 see block lyric)

____   look-ing for__ a rea - son,   to find__ her life's place.__

____ Feel-ing a lit - tle bit sad,   but not real-ly all that

but she still can't hide,_____ she can't leave her life right.

℅ *CHORUS*

Trapped by— her life,_____ (Love is unavoidable) just to— get by.—

_____ (To make it more affordable) Trapped by— her life,_____ (Love is unavoidable)

just to— get by._____ (To make it more affordable) Can't af - ford that,

Verse 2:
She looks in the mirror
Her reflection's someone old
Seeing days go by
She don't need to be told.
Feeling a little bit sad
She cries and packs her bags
Remembering a dream
A dream that she'll never have.

Where will she go?
(But it ain't that easy)
How long till she comes home?
(But it's all too sleazy)
Maybe she'll make it
Will she…
…or maybe not.

Beg

Words & Music by Jonathan Douglas, Shaznay Lewis,
John Benson, Ralph MacDonald & William Slater

(If you're searching forgiveness.) Gon - na give it to me.

(On the floor where I can see.) On your knees and beg.

(If you're searching forgiveness.) Got - ta, you got - ta,

got-ta, you got-ta, got-ta you got-ta.

Won't let no-bo-dy bring me down.

Tell-ing you what goes a-round, comes a-round.

Life's just full of mys - te - ries, that's ex - act-

- ly what you are, ex - act-ly what you are to me.

Get down on your knees,

gon - na give it to me.

Got-ta, you got-ta, got-ta, you got-ta,

got-ta, you got-ta.

Today's letter was 'B'
and the word was 'beg.'

Lady Marmalade

Words & Music by Bob Crewe & Kenny Nolan

Hey sis-ter, go sis-ter, soul sis-ter, go sis-ter.

Hey sis - ter, go sis - ter, soul sis - ter, go sis - ter. Hey sis - ter, go sis - ter,

soul sis - ter, go sis - ter. Hey sis - ter, go sis - ter, soul sis - ter, go sis - ter.

(2.) come on and share___ all your deep___ fan - ta - sies,___ I'm
(1.3. spoken see block lyric)

ask - ing, not tell - ing you please,___ Show me all night___ you can do___

✛ *Coda*

Repeat to fade

Verse 1: (spoken)

Do you fancy enough, hit him in the sack
Yes my kitty cat is a wreck
And then some, you are the one
Gotta represent, gotta go the whole run.
We can play all night, gotta do it right
Snuggle up, huddle up, nice and tight
My place or yours, gotta be raw
Don't really matter once we get through the door.

Verse 3: (spoken)

Mocca chocolata ha
Coucher ce soir
Run, run that's right
Bring it on daddy it's the bedroom fight.
Get ahead, get your drawers and put them on fast
Got to keep up if you think you can last
Gonna get wet, are you ready yet?
On your marks, get set.

Take The Key

Words & Music by Shaznay Lewis
Music by Karl Gordon, Kirk Robinson & Nathaniel Robinson

Take the key and you'll find,___

lov - ing you makes me feel.___

Oh___

I hold a key in___ my heart.___ You know it's true when

(Verse 2 see block lyric)

Tacet 1°

Verse 2:
Yeah, time stood still
The way I feel would be
Unconditional, eternal, everlasting
Oh you know that I feel complete.

War Of Nerves

Words & Music by Shaznay Lewis, Melanie Blatt,
Natalie Appleton, Nicole Appleton, Cameron McVey & Magnus Fiennes

Mon-day on the line,
(Verse 2 see block lyric)

when you know that now's the time, to leave and be free a-

call my name.

I don't ev - ver want to feel___ fear,_____ 'cause

ev - 'ry night feels al - right

when you're near.

2.

near.___

Don't wan - na be   like a   voice with - out

words.

Don't wan - na be   a - lone in this

Verse 2:
Battle through this war of nerves
When your life, it takes a turn
And what I have is what I fear
While in my mind you're lying here.
Feel that unholy dread
There's a piece of me in all he says
All kinds of mixed-up inside my head
This stage fright in my own bed.

At B final choruses:
2
I don't ever want to feel pain
When it's over, will I feel the same?
I don't ever want to feel fear
This war of nerves that I reserve
For when you're here.

3
I don't ever want to feel pain
I'm feeling hurt but I feel no shame
I don't ever want to feel fear
Do I deserve these cruel words
We have here?